PUFFIN BOOKS

FIVE FURRY T
A COLLECTIO
ACTION RHYM
SONGS AND GAMES

Five Furry Teddy Bears brings a bright new contemporary
approach to one of the most important parts of a young child's
world – learning through play. There are well over a hundred
poems, games, action rhymes and finger plays on a whole
variety of themes, including seasons and special days, counting
and telling the time, home and outdoor activities (including
road safety), and learning basic skills, such as cleaning teeth,
having a bath, and posting a letter. Then there's also the world
of make-believe, with dragon hunts, trips on magic carpets,
journeys into space and pirate adventures.

This book provides the perfect modern complement to
traditional collections of action rhymes and is an essential
addition to every parent's and teacher's bookshelf.

Linda Hammond was born in Birmingham, and educated at
Trinity Hall, Southport and Eastbourne High School for Girls.
Having trained as a nursery nurse, Linda decided to open the
Humpty Dumpty Playgroup in Chelmsford, which she ran for
eleven years. During this time she also tutored for the
Pre-school Playgroups Association and contributed daily
features for under-fives on local radio. Linda Hammond is a
foster parent and now lives with her family in the West Country
where, as well as her writing, she enjoys running the Tom
Thumb Playgroup for the South Devon College of Arts and
Technology.

LINDA HAMMOND

FIVE
FURRY
TEDDY
BEARS
A Collection of Contemporary
Action Rhymes,
Finger Plays,
Songs and Games

Illustrated by Julie Park
Music arranged by Sandra Walker

PUFFIN BOOKS

PUFFIN BOOKS

Published by the Penguin Group
27 Wrights Lane, London W8 5TZ, England
Viking Penguin Inc., 40 West 23rd Street, New York, New York 10010, USA
Penguin Books Australia Ltd, Ringwood, Victoria, Australia
Penguin Books Canada Ltd, 2801 John Street, Markham, Ontario,
Canada L3R 1B4
Penguin Books (NZ) Ltd, 182–190 Wairau Road, Auckland 10, New Zealand

Penguin Books Ltd, Registered Offices: Harmondsworth, Middlesex, England

First published 1990
10 9 8 7 6 5 4 3 2 1

Text and original music copyright © Linda Hammond, 1990
Illustrations copyright © Julie Park, 1990
Music arrangement copyright © Sandra Walker, 1990
All rights reserved

Made and printed in Great Britain by Cox and Wyman Ltd, Reading, Berks.

Filmset in Linotron Times by
Rowland Phototypesetting Ltd, Bury St Edmunds, Suffolk

To Humpty and Co. with love

CONTENTS

AT HOME

DOWN OUR STREET

BESIDE THE SEASIDE

FAIRGROUND FUN

IN THE COUNTRY

CREEPY-CRAWLIES

HELLO ME

PLAYTIME

THE WORLD OF ADVENTURE

INTRODUCTION

Many years ago when I first started working with young children, I was introduced to Elizabeth Matterson's wonderful compilation volume of nursery rhymes and songs called *This Little Puffin* . . . Time and again, it provided just the verse I was looking for, but there were occasions when it did not. Consequently, after many hours of unsuccessful searching through shelves of poetry and song-books in both libraries and shops to find other similarly stimulating material, I decided there was nothing else for it but to sit down and write my own. One notebook of random scribbling soon became two, and then three, and it occurred to me that perhaps other children and adults might enjoy playing the games as well. So the notebooks were amalgamated, the contents shuffled and *Five Furry Teddy Bears* came into being.

But why do I think rhymes, games and songs are so important for young children? After all, there are plenty of other things for them to do. In the first place, they are fun because they enable both adults and children to play together. Secondly, by using simple words in rhythmic patterns, the children effortlessly absorb and retain the new ideas and vocabulary presented to them. Some of the material like 'Growing' or 'Doing the Washing' extends the children's knowledge about the world in which they live, while other rhymes like 'Crackers' and 'Five Bananas' provide the opportunity for counting, adding or subtracting. Social skills such as sharing, taking turns, accepting disappointment or enjoying success are also very much part and parcel of this valuable time together.

By listening and learning, children's powers of concentration and their confidence and ability to communicate are all increased, providing further evidence, if any is still needed, that rhymes, songs and games have a great part to play in the growth and development of children.

It is important to be confident as you share the collection with your children. If you are enthusiastic and make it sound fun, they will enjoy it too. I have included practical instructions on how to play, but your own interpretation is fine. Don't worry if you can't sing – it's the ideas that matter. Capture the child's imagination and your dramatic or vocal ability becomes irrelevant.

Just remember that whether it's with a large number of children at playgroup or simply you and your child at home, the main aim is to enjoy yourselves.

I hope you have fun.

Linda Hammond

ROUND
THE
YEAR

GROWING

I'm going, I'm going, I'm going –
> *Kneel on floor with hands as if praying and*
> *curl up tightly.*

now I know how it feels to be growing.
> *Straighten back very, very slowly.*

First the tips of my leaves push up through
the ground,
> *Push hands up gradually until level with*
> *chin.*

quietly, so quietly they don't make a sound.
> *Put one finger to lips.*

I stop for a rest, then down comes the rain,
> *Fold arms, then indicate rain with fingers.*

my leaves have a drink, then I'm growing
again.
> *Cup hands and pretend to drink. Continue*
> *growing.*

If the sun starts to shine, my leaves open
wide,
> *Move arms upwards and outwards to*
> *indicate sun shining and leaves opening.*

but when the wind blows they all try to hide.
> *Clasp arms overhead and sway from side to*
> *side.*

I've roots at the bottom and leaves on top –
   Point to feet, then head.
I'm growing and growing, but when will I
   stop?
   Stand up slowly.
Perhaps I'm a flower, a bush or a tree –
   Use hand to show the different plant heights.
what do you think I am going to be?
   Point to child opposite, then to yourself.
   Discuss answer.

HOW TO PLAY

Set the scene by explaining that seeds have been planted in the ground and are now beginning to grow. Children form two lines facing each other, with an adult both sides if possible.

HEDGEHOG WAKES UP

The win-ter _ is o - ver, _ the spring has now _ come. I've

just wo - ken up so _ I think I'll _ have fun! But

first to make sure that _ my bo - dy's _ all - right, 'cause

I have been sleep-ing _ for more than _ one night. My

back is _ all stiff and _ my legs are _____ too, so

this is what I'm go - ing _____ to do—

Jump, jump, jump, jump, jump, jump, jump.

The winter is over, the spring has now come.
I've just woken up, so I think I'll have fun!
But first to make sure that my body's all
    right,
'cause I have been sleeping for more than one
    night.
My back is all stiff and my legs are too,
so this is what I'm going to do –

Jump, jump, jump, jump, jump, jump,
    jump.
OR stretch, bend, crawl, hop, walk, run,
    dance, etc.

Children mime the actions suggested by the words using maximum space available.

THE BIRD IS ON HER NEST

(Tune: Farmer's in His Den)

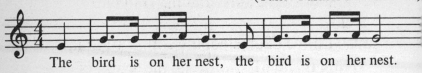

The bird is on her nest, the bird is on her nest.

Tweet, tweet, tweet, tweet, the bird is on her nest.

1. The bird is on her nest,
   the bird is on her nest.
   Tweet, tweet, tweet, tweet,
   the bird is on her nest.

2. She has laid some eggs, etc.

3. The eggs begin to hatch, etc.

4. The babies want some food, etc.

5. Daddy brings some worms, etc.

6. They all eat the worms, etc.

HOW TO PLAY

Choose one child to be the Daddy
bird, who waits to one side. Then
choose another child to be the
Mummy bird, who sits in the centre of
a circle formed by the other players
holding hands.

Verse 1:
Circle right. At end of verse, three
children are chosen by the 'Mummy
bird' to be her eggs. They curl up on
the floor in the centre.

[cont.]

Verse 2:
Circle left. 'Mummy bird' flies round
'eggs'.

Verse 3:
Stand still, facing inwards and clap
while 'chicks' gradually break out of
their shells and stand up.

Verse 4:
Circle right. 'Daddy bird' flies into
'nest' and dances with family, leaving
at the end of the verse.

Verse 5:
Circle left. 'Daddy bird' flies round
the outside, while bird family dances
round together in the centre. At end
of verse, 'Daddy bird' re-enters 'nest'.

Verse 6:
Stand still, facing inwards and clap as
'Daddy bird' feeds the hungry chicks.

TADPOLES

In a pond beneath some trees
five tadpoles swam about.
Wriggle, squiggle, wriggle, squiggle,
then a frog jumped out!

In a pond beneath some trees
four tadpoles swam about.
Wriggle, squiggle, wriggle, squiggle,
then a frog jumped out!

In a pond beneath some trees
three tadpoles swam about.
Wriggle, squiggle, wriggle, squiggle,
then a frog jumped out!

[cont.]

In a pond beneath some trees
two tadpoles swam about.
Wriggle, squiggle, wriggle, squiggle,
then a frog jumped out!

In a pond beneath some trees
one tadpole swam about.
Wriggle, squiggle, wriggle, squiggle,
then a frog jumped out!

*Children or fingers may be used to
represent the tadpoles/frogs.*

DAFFODILS

Ten golden daffodils
dancing in the sun.
A naughty dog came running by
and knocked down one.

9, 8, 7, 6, etc.

*Children or fingers may be used to
represent the daffodils.*

EASTER EGGS

Easter eggs – Easter eggs,
five in a row.
Each wrapped up in paper
and tied with a bow.
All made of chocolate,
creamy and sweet –
I'll just nibble one (nibble, nibble),
leaving (four) still to eat.

                              4, 3, 2, 1.

*Children or fingers may be used to
represent the Easter eggs.*

25

RAINBOWS

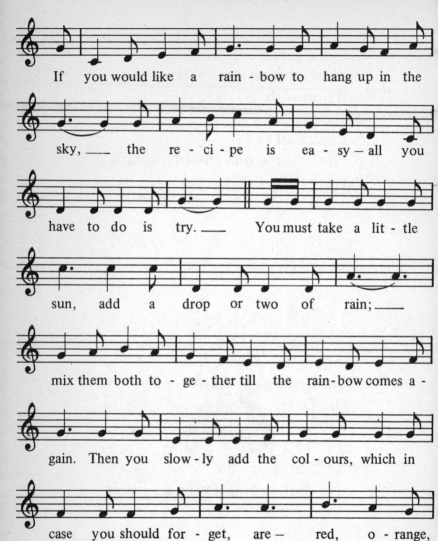

If you would like a rain-bow to hang up in the sky, ___ the re-ci-pe is ea-sy — all you have to do is try. ___ You must take a lit-tle sun, add a drop or two of rain; ___ mix them both to-ge-ther till the rain-bow comes a-gain. Then you slow-ly add the col-ours, which in case you should for-get, are — red, o-range,

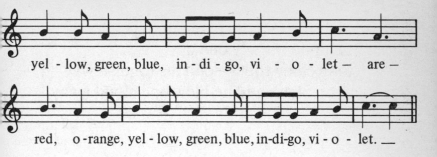

yel - low, green, blue, in - di - go, vi - o - let — are —

red, o -range, yel - low, green, blue, in-di-go, vi - o - let. —

If you would like a rainbow
to hang up in the sky,
the recipe is easy –
all you have to do is try.

CHORUS
You must take a little sun,
add a drop or two of rain;
mix them both together
till the rainbow comes again.
Then you slowly add the colours,
which in case you should forget,
are – red, orange, yellow, green,
blue, indigo, violet –
are – red, orange, yellow, green,
blue, indigo, violet.

CLOUDS

Five fluffy clouds came out to play
high up in the sky one day.
Along came the wind in his roguish way
and he blew, and he blew one cloud away!

4, 3, 2, 1.

*Children or fingers may be used to
represent the clouds.*

YOUR SHADOW

Along the ground
without a sound
your shadow follows you.
It copies every move you make
and everything you do!
It runs, it walks,
it waves its arms,
and even nods its head.
But when there is no source of light,
your shadow goes to bed!

*Children may like to mime the actions
suggested by the words.*

A WINDY DAY

Round and round the washing-line goes –
over and over twist all the clothes.
Sometimes they're fat and sometimes thin
as the wind comes out, then blows back in!

Round and over and in and out,
the wind is blowing things about.

The wind blows here, the wind blows there,
making fallen leaves dance everywhere.
Down on the ground, then up in the sky.
Some twirling low and then whirling high.

Round and over and in and out,
the wind is blowing things about.

Children have fun and children chase
as the wild wind blows from place to place.
It tickles faces and tangles hair,
but neither the wind nor children care!

Round and over and in and out,
the wind is blowing things about.

*Using maximum space available, mime the
actions suggested by the words.*

SIGNS OF AUTUMN

The days are getting shorter,
some birds have flown away,
and farmers have been harvesting
from dawn till dusk each day.
Children have returned to school,
and leaves have changed to brown,
ready for the autumn winds
to come and blow them down!

Children may like to be birds,
farmers, etc.

HALLOWE'EN PUMPKINS

Five pumpkin faces in the night,
glowing orange candle-light.
Hallowe'en – no time for tears!
Just blow, and one face disappears!

4, 3, 2, 1.

Children or fingers may be used to
represent the pumpkins.

RAINDROPS

(Tune: I Had a Little Nut Tree)

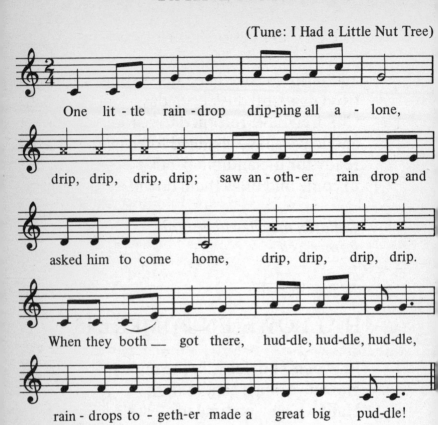

One little raindrop dripping all alone,
drip, drip, drip, drip;
saw another raindrop and asked him to come
    home,
drip, drip, drip, drip.

When they both got there,
huddle, huddle, huddle,
raindrops together made a great big puddle!

HOW TO PLAY

Lines 1–3:
Choose one child to represent 'raindrop', who skips round the outside of a moving circle formed by the other players holding hands, facing outwards.

Line 4:
Stand still while 'raindrop' chooses a friend to go with him/her into the centre of the circle where they dance round together.

Lines 5–7:
Remaining players face inwards,
link arms and 'huddle' round in opposite direction.

REPEAT until the puddle in the centre gets too big!

LITTLE SNOWMAN

(Traditional/adapted)

I'm a lit - tle snow - man white and fat.

Here's my pipe and here's my hat.

I've got but - tons one, two, three.

Will you count them all with me?

One two three. I'm a lit -tle snow-man white and fat.

Don't throw snow - balls at my hat!

If you do I'll turn a - round and

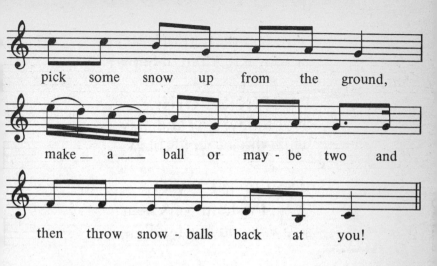

pick some snow up from the ground,

make — a — ball or may - be two and

then throw snow - balls back at you!

I'm a little snowman
white and fat.
Here's my pipe and here's my hat.
I've got buttons – one, two, three.
Will you count them all with me?
One – two – three.
I'm a little snowman
white and fat.
Don't throw snowballs at my hat!
If you do I'll turn around
and pick some snow up from the ground,
make a ball or maybe two
and then throw snowballs back at you!

Mime the actions suggested by the words.

POLAR BEAR

'Are you there, Polar Bear,
in your Kingdom of Snow?'

RESPONSE ONE
'Not today, stay and play
while the icy winds blow.'

RESPONSE TWO
'Yes, I'm here, very near
so away you must go!'

HOW TO PLAY

'Polar Bear' hides under
chair or similar object.
Explorers approach asking
question. 'Polar Bear' varies
his/her response. Explorers
act accordingly!

WHO WAS IN THE STABLE?

Who was in the stable
that Christmas first of all?
Jesus, Mummy Mary,
and Joseph standing tall.
Then there were some shepherds,
two and then two more.
To make it ten,
three tired Wise Men
came knocking at the door!

*Use both hands for this finger
rhyme.*

SANTA'S SACK

It's getting near to Christmas,
so let's help Santa pack,
all the toys for girls and boys
into his great big sack.

(Soldiers) Are you ready?
Then (march) round one, two, three.

What lovely Christmas presents,
we know you're going to be.

HOW TO PLAY

Join hands in a circle and walk round
while singing first two lines. Release
hands, face centre and pretend to fill
the sack. A toy is suggested, then all
move round in a circle miming
appropriate actions. For example
teddies dance, rabbits hop, sports cars
race, ponies gallop (omit 'round').

THE CHRISTMAS TREE

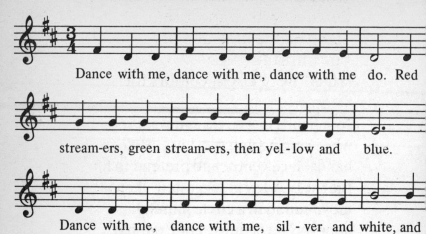

Dance with me, dance with me, dance with me do. Red
stream-ers, green stream-ers, then yel - low and blue.
Dance with me, dance with me, sil - ver and white, and

help make our Christ - mas tree pret - ty to - night.

Dance with me, dance with me,
dance with me do.
Red streamers, green streamers,
then yellow and blue.
Dance with me, dance with me,
silver and white,
and help make our Christmas tree
pretty tonight.

(Red) streamers, (red) streamers,
stand on a chair.

40

Right up on tiptoe,
don't wobble! Take care!
Hang on the branches of
our Christmas tree –
what lovely bright colours for
people to see.

HOW TO PLAY

Verse 1
a) A real or substitute Christmas
tree is placed with up to four very
stable chairs around it.
b) Each child is then given a
coloured streamer to wave as they
dance round the tree. No more than
four of each colour (red, green,
yellow, blue, silver and white) to be used.

Verse 2
a) Children holding the coloured
streamers stand on the chairs and
decorate the tree, while the others
watch and wave their real, or if
already relinquished, pretend
streamers overhead.
b) Gradually all the streamers are

[cont.]

put on to the 'tree', either as
individual colours or all together
when the game reaches its natural
conclusion.

CRACKERS

Ten Christmas crackers
on the Christmas tree.
Ten Christmas crackers
on the Christmas tree.
If I give two away,
and leave the rest for me,
how many crackers are there
on the Christmas tree?

Let's pull them together.
Pull–pull–pull–pull
pull–pull   BANG!

                    8, 6, 4, 2.

In order to help children
appreciate the mathematical
connotations of this rhyme,
suggest visual aids are used.

CARDS TO POST

Here are ten Christmas cards ready to send
to people I like most.
(Name) would you help me please
and take this card to post?

9, 8, 7, 6, etc.

*Children in turn take real or substitute cards to
improvised post-box.*

ICICLES

Five long icicles hanging on a wall,
but as the sun begins to shine,
one melts and starts to fall.

Drip – drip – drip – CRASH.

4, 3, 2, 1.

*Children or fingers may be used to
represent the icicles.*

MAGIC
AND
MAKE-
BELIEVE

THE MAGIC CARPET

We have found a ma - gic car - pet, so we're
go - ing for a ride. Fly - ing o - ver
moun-tain tops, towns and coun -try - side. To
get the ma-gic work-ing we will have to weave a
spell. All on knees then qui - et please, we
want it to work well. Can-dle - light, gold- en
bright, work your ma -gic spell of night. Gen-tle

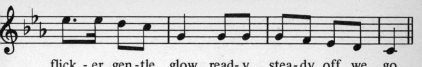

flick - er, gen -tle glow, read- y, stea- dy, off we go.

We have found a magic carpet,
so we're going for a ride.
> *Children join hands in a circle and walk
> slowly round in time to the music.*

Flying over mountain tops,
towns and countryside.
> *Move towards centre, raising arms as you go
> (mountains) and return.*

To get the magic working
we will have to weave a spell.
> *Children join hands in a circle and walk
> slowly round in time to the music.*

All on knees, then quiet please,
we want it to work well.
> *Turn towards centre and kneel. Put fingers
> up to lips.*

[cont.]

SPELL

Candle-light, golden bright,
work your magic spell of night.
Gentle flicker, gentle glow,
ready, steady, off we go.

> *Adult moves round the inside of the circle,
> showing children real or substitute candle.
> When the word 'night' is reached, child
> nearest the 'candle' climbs aboard the magic
> carpet for an adult-assisted flight round the
> outside of the ring. All wave!*

PLEASE NOTE
*A magic carpet is needed for this game! If
unobtainable, any of the following could be used:
old tea trolley, pram, pushchair covered with a
travelling rug, blanket, etc. Alternatively sit child
on rug.*

LOOKING FOR DRAGONS

What shall we do on Sunday?
Look for dragons.
What shall we do on Monday?
Look for dragons.
What shall we do on Tuesday?
Look for dragons.
What shall we do on Wednesday?
Look for dragons.
What shall we do on Thursday?
Look for dragons.
What shall we do on Friday?
Look for dragons.
What shall we do on Saturday?
Run away!

HOW TO PLAY

Children follow an adult slowly up
the room asking the various
questions. Adult replies 'Look for
dragons', but occasionally surprises
everyone by telling them to 'Run
Away!'

A SECRET

Can you keep a secret?
Promise not to tell.
Last week I saw a mermaid,
sitting in a shell.
I'm sure it was a mermaid –
it had a fishy tail.
But then perhaps on second thoughts,
it might have been a snail!

HUNGRY ELVES

An elf sat on a toadstool
eating bread and cheese.
A hungry friend jumped up and said,
'Could I have some please?'

Two elves, etc.

*Children or fingers may be used to
represent the elves.*

FIVE WICKED WITCHES

Five wicked witches sitting on a broom,
five wicked witches sitting on a broom,
and if one wicked witch tried to make more
  room,
there'd be four wicked witches sitting on the
  broom.

4, 3, 2, 1.

HOW TO PLAY

Five children sit side-saddle on real or pretend
broomstick. As the rhyme progresses, number of
witches reduced by each child elbowing the next
in turn, until the last one is 'pushed off' the end
of the broomstick. (This may also be sung to
'Ten Green Bottles'.)

THE ROBOT

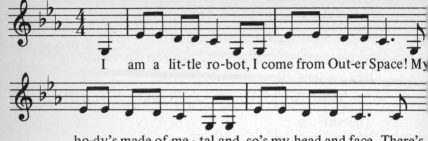

I am a lit-tle ro-bot, I come from Out-er Space! My

bo-dy's made of me - tal and so's my head and face. There's

lots of wires in -side me and knobs and switch-es too, so

if you press this but - ton you'll see what I can do!

STARTING POSITION

*Find space, stand still. Bend over until hands
are level with knees, keeping legs straight.*

I am a little robot,

*Raise body slowly and stiffly with arms
outstretched in front to shoulder level.*

I come from Outer Space!

*Keeping arms stiff, indicate 'Outer Space' to
left and right.*

My body's made of metal
> *With rigid movements, touch shoulders,*
> *tummy, knees and toes.*

and so's my head and face.
> *With rigid movements, touch head and face.*

There's lots of wires inside me
> *Make circular movements near chest with*
> *fingers.*

and knobs and switches too,
> *Touch each elbow and back of head.*

so if you press this button
> *Press nose.*

you'll see what I can do!
> *Revert slowly to starting position.*

I start off very slowly,
turn head from side to side,
and then my arms begin to move
out straight and then spread wide.
My legs transport me forwards,
together then apart.
Clank, clank, clank, clank, clank, clank,
    clank,
right back to the start!

Adopt starting position, then follow all other
directions with mechanical movements.

SPACEMEN

In — si - lent sau - cers we pass the stars, we—

slide down the Mil — ky Way. ____ We're —

men from Sa - turn, Plu - to and Mars on —

Earth — for just one day. ____ We

look and we lis - ten, we smile and laugh, ____

— and then we fly a - way! ____

In silent saucers we pass the stars,
> *Move freely around room, with arms in*
> *flight position.*

we slide down the Milky Way.
> *Stand still, put hands together palms*
> *downwards and move arms briskly as if*
> *going down a slide.*

We're men from Saturn, Pluto and Mars
> *Point arms to indicate different directions of*
> *the named planets.*

on Earth for just one day.
> *Point to Earth and raise index finger to*
> *represent one day.*

We look and we listen,
> *Ring eyes with index fingers and thumbs,*
> *then cup ears with hands.*

we smile and laugh,
> *Draw smile on face with finger – laugh.*

and then we fly away!
> *Move freely around room, with arms in flight*
> *position.*

GIANT MISTAKE

Giant Mistake was a jovial fellow.
His shoes were red, and his shirt was yellow.
His legs were long, and with arms spread
   wide,
he could hold six houses side by side.

Giant Mistake every morning would stride
over towns and cities and countryside.
He'd smile and he'd wave and shout 'Hello'
to the tiny people far below!

*Suggest children may enjoy bringing this poem to
life by using doll's house/play people, etc.*

AT
HOME

THE OLD HOUSE

Verses 1, 3, 5

I am an old, old house and I've

ro - ses round the door, a

thatched roof with a chim - ney and a

Verses 2, 4

wib - bly, wob - bly floor. I've got

ti - ny criss - cross win - dows ___ which

peep through i - vy leaves

watch - ing swal - lows fly - ing ___ and

nest - ing in the eaves.

I am an old, old house
and I've roses round the door,
a thatched roof with a chimney
and a wibbly, wobbly floor.

I've got tiny criss-cross windows
which peep through ivy leaves –
watching swallows flying
and nesting in the eaves.

Inside my rooms are small
and the ceilings very low,
with wooden beams in plenty
where brasses hang on show.

I've a great big open fireplace
for burning logs and coal.
Rocking chairs to sit in,
dried flowers in a bowl.

I am an old, old house
and I've roses round the door,
a thatched roof with a chimney
and a wibbly, wobbly floor.

BOTTLES OF MILK

Clink, clink, clin - ke - ty, clink; we're

bot - tles of milk for you to drink. We

stand up tall, we stand up straight,

rea - dy and wait - ing in our crate. The

milk - man has his job to do, he

has to bring the milk to you; he

goes to the crate and takes out two —

emp - ty   bot - tles   form   a   queue.

Clink, clink, clinkety, clink;
we're bottles of milk for you to drink.
We stand up tall,
we stand up straight,
ready and waiting in our crate.
The milkman has his job to do,
he has to bring the milk to you;
he goes to the crate
and takes out two –
empty bottles
form a queue.

HOW TO PLAY

Choose a child to be the milkman, who
waits to one side. The remaining
players, who represent bottles of milk,
form a circle holding hands.

[cont.]

Lines 1–2:
Starting with feet together, slide left foot to side, then right foot together. Repeat.

Line 3:
Stand still facing inwards, stretch arms high.

Line 4:
Stand up straight, arms to side.

Line 5:
Stand up straight, arms folded.

Line 6 onwards:
Clap while 'milkman' goes round the outside of circle (crate). He then chooses, removes and delivers two bottles of milk to a pre-determined destination, where they remain until collected and returned to the crate next time round. Change 'milkman'.

PANCAKES

Pancakes, pancakes, pancakes for tea.
Who'd like to make some pancakes with me?
We'll mix them and beat them
and toss them once more.
Oh no! Mine's just landed
face down on the floor!

Mime actions suggested by the words.

DOING THE WASHING

I put my (trousers)
in the washing machine.
(It/they) went in dirty
and (it/they) came out clean.

I stood on tiptoe
and stretched up high,
and hung (it/them) on the line
to dry.

I took (it/them) in
and ironed with care.
Now once again
(It's/they're) fit to wear.

*Children suggest item of
clothing to be washed, then
mime the rhyme.*

WRITING LETTERS

Writing letters, writing letters,
pencil in my hand.
Scribble, scribble, scribble,
I hope you'll understand.

Drawing pictures, drawing pictures,
colours red, green, blue.
Squiggles, circles, splodges
especially for you.

Posting letters, posting letters,
envelopes in hand.
Each one with a stamp on
to travel over land.

MAKING BREAD

Verses 1, 3, 5, 7

Let's pre-tend to make some bread, make some bread, make some bread. Let's pre-tend to make some bread on this (Mon-day) morn-ing.

Verses 2, 4, 6

First of all we'll weigh the flo-ur, weigh the flo-ur, weigh the flo-ur. First of all we'll weigh the flo-ur on this (Mon-day) morn-ing.

Let's pretend to make some bread,
make some bread – make some bread.
Let's pretend to make some bread
on this (Monday) morning.

First of all we'll weigh the flour,
weigh the flour – weigh the flour.
First of all we'll weigh the flour
on this (Monday) morning.

Now we have to add the yeast,
add the yeast – add the yeast.
Now we have to add the yeast
on this (Monday) morning.

[cont.]

Let us pour some water in,
some water in – some water in.
Let us pour some water in
on this (Monday) morning.

Bump and thump and knead the dough,
knead the dough – knead the dough.
Bump and thump and knead the dough
on this (Monday) morning.

Put on tray in oven to bake,
oven to bake – oven to bake.
Put on tray in oven to bake
on this (Monday) morning.

Cut and spread the bread to eat,
bread to eat – bread to eat.
Cut and spread the bread to eat
on this (Monday) morning

Mime the actions suggested by the words.

CLOCK IN THE HALL

'Clock in the hall
standing so tall,
what do you do all day?'
'I tell you the time
on each hour with a
chime.
Listen to hear what I say!'

Clap number of hours.

FRED BUMBLE

(Tune: Old MacDonald)

When old Fred Bum-ble had a bath, he had lots of fun. He would turn both taps on full, and watch the wa-ter run. With a splash, splash, here, and a splash, splash, there. Here a splash, there a splash, eve-ry-where a splash, splash! When old Fred Bum-ble had a bath, he had lots of fun!

When old Fred Bumble had a bath,
he had lots of fun.

He would turn both taps on full,
and watch the water run.

CHORUS
With a splash, splash, here,
and a splash, splash, there.
Here a splash, there a splash,
everywhere a splash, splash!
When old Fred Bumble had a bath,
he had lots of fun!

When old Fred Bumble had a bath,
water to the top.
Higher, higher watch it come,
would it ever stop?

CHORUS

When old Fred Bumble had a bath,
he'd wash from head to toe.
Then he'd pull the plug right out,
and watch the water go.

CHORUS

*To enjoy this song, exuberant actions
are called for.*

BATHTIME

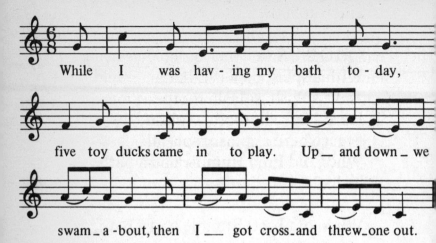

While I was having my bath today,
five toy ducks came in to play.
Up and down we swam about,
then I got cross and threw one out!

4, 3, 2, 1.

While I was having my bath today,
no toy ducks came in to play.
I was sad and asked for more.
'No,' said Daddy, 'they stay on the floor!'

HOW TO PLAY

This may be played with the fingers of one hand. Alternatively, players holding hands move round in a circle with bathing child and ducks in centre, miming the actions suggested by the words. Substitute the child's name, etc. as necessary. For example, 'While (Paul) was having (his) bath today'.

BEDTIME

'Ready, Teddy, time for bed!'
Naughty Teddy shook his head.
Went and hid behind a chair,
hoped I wouldn't find him there.
But I did!
So I took him up the stairs,
washed him, listened to his prayers.
Tucked him up, turned off the light,
kissed him twice, and said 'Good-night'.

DOWN
OUR
STREET

LOLLIPOP LADY

(Calypso

I'm a Lol - li - pop La - dy with a lol - li - pop. My

job is to make all the traf - fic __ stop. I

stand in the road with my stick held high and

watch as the child -ren go safe - ly by.

Chorus

Lol-li - pop La - dy, __ La - dy am I, _____ I

watch as the child-ren go safe - ly by.

I'm a Lollipop Lady with a lollipop.
My job is to make all the traffic stop.
I stand in the road with my stick held high
and watch as the children go safely by.

CHORUS
Lollipop Lady, Lady am I,
I watch as the children go safely by.

Double-decker bus, bike, lorry, van or car –
it doesn't really matter what they are.
If they see my stick, then they have to stop,
'cause I am the lady with the lollipop!

CHORUS
Lollipop Lady, Lady am I,
I watch as the children go safely by.

No matter what the weather, snow, sunshine
    or rain,
when children go to school, I'm there again,
holding up my stick for people to see.
All drivers and walkers, they must obey me!

CHORUS
Lollipop Lady, Lady am I,
I watch as the children go safely by.

This song has scope for active participation.

AT THE SUPERMARKET

No stopping! No stopping!
We're doing the shopping.
There's lots of things to buy.
(Eggs) on the low shelves,
(Bread) on the middle,
and for (soap) we have to reach high.

No breaking! No spilling!
Our trolleys we're filling
with things we need today.
At checkouts we queue,
wait, pay and go through.
We then take our shopping away!

*Mime the actions suggested by the
words.*

ROAD MAKING

First of all we'll dig a hole,
fill it in, then roll, roll, roll.
Spray with tar and gravel too,
roll, roll, roll the whole day through.
Now we need some traffic signs,
kerbs and drains and long white lines,
some Cats'-eyes which reflect the light
to help all drivers see at night.
A roundabout where four roads meet
and zebra crossings for our feet.
Then traffic lights – green, amber, red
attached to posts, and overhead.
Along the verge plant trees to grow –
the road is finished, time to go!

*Use hands and visual aids, e.g. traffic
signs as appropriate.*

BUILDING

Let us build a bungalow,
one brick on the floor.
Let us build a house now,
we just need one brick more.
Let us build some flats now,
towering to the sky,
brick on brick, brick on brick,
several storeys high.

*Build using clenched hands or
bricks/wooden blocks.*

DO YOU KNOW WHERE YOU LIVE?

Do you know where you live?
I really think you should.
That your door is painted blue,
I'm sorry is no good!
You need to know the *number*
of your home, your house or flat,
and what your *road* or street's called,
and the *town's* name after that.
If you can learn these three things,
which all make up your address,
when asked if you know where you live,
the answer will be 'yes'.

LET'S ALL RIDE OUR BICYCLES

Let's all ride our bi - cy - cles,   pedal-ling fast, then slow.

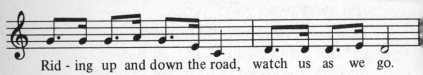

Rid - ing up and down the road,   watch us   as   we   go.

Let's all ride our bicycles,
pedalling fast, then slow.
Riding up and down the road,
watch us as we go.

Let's all drive our motor cars,
sometimes fast, then slow.
Driving up and down the road,
watch us as we go.

Let's all drive our lorries now,
when empty fast – then slow.
Carrying concrete up the road,
watch us as we go.

Cars and lorries everywhere.
Dear me, what a fuss.
We're not driving any more,
we're going on the bus!

Mime the actions suggested by the words.

STREET FRIENDS

When we go walking down the street,
there's five street friends for us to meet.

'Hello, postbox.
What do you do?'
'I collect letters two by two.'

'Hello, lamppost.
What do you do?'
'I shine my light the whole night
through.'

'Hello, phone box.
What do you do?'
'I'm here so friends can talk to you.'

'Hello, signpost.
What do you do?'
'I point to places: town or zoo.'

'Hello, traffic lights.
What do you do?'
'I let cars go, then stop a few.'

Five street friends all in a row –
clap your hands and away they go!

HOW TO PLAY

Choose five children to represent the street friends mentioned, and position them at intervals in a line down the room. The remaining children and adults visit each in turn and ask the appropriate question. Initially help may be required with the response, but a spontaneous answer is quite acceptable! This may also be played as a finger rhyme.

GOOD MORNING

'Good morning.'

'Good morning.'

'How are you today?'

'Not very happy!'

'Why's that?'

'I cannot say.'

'Maybe I can help you.'

'How? What will you do?'

'Close your eyes.'

'They're tightly shut.'

'Now, if you're ready – BOO!'

HOW TO PLAY

Initially two adults, with two
children as 'shadows' behind,
walk towards each other. Stop,
shake hands on 'Good
morning', then continue
speaking alternate lines.
Appropriate 'shadow' closes
eyes, and the other 'shadow'
jumps out on the word 'Boo!'

CROSSING THE ROAD

(Tune: Head and Shoulders)

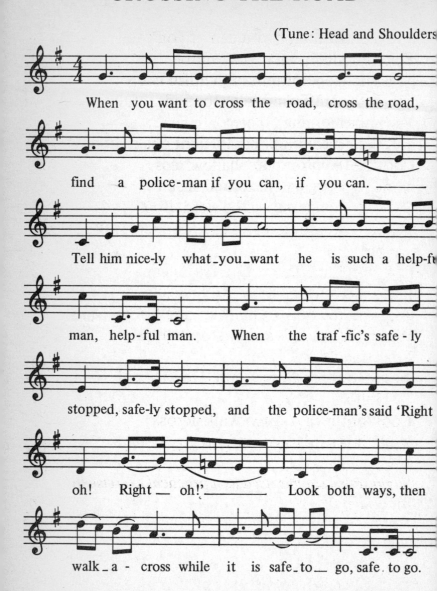

When you want to cross the road, cross the road,

find a police-man if you can, if you can. _____

Tell him nice-ly what_you_want he is such a help-fu

man, help-ful man. When the traf-fic's safe-ly

stopped, safe-ly stopped, and the police-man's said 'Right

oh! Right _ oh!' _____ Look both ways, then

walk _ a - cross while it is safe_to_ go, safe. to go.

When you want to cross the road, cross the
   road,
find a policeman if you can, if you can.
Tell him nicely what you want –
he is such a helpful man, helpful man.
When the traffic's safely stopped, safely
   stopped,
and the policeman's said 'Right oh, right oh!'
Look both ways, then walk across
while it is safe to go, safe to go.

When you want to cross the road, cross the
   road,
find a crossing if you can, if you can.
Press the button, stand well back,
and wait for the Green Man, the Green Man.
When the traffic's safely stopped, safely
   stopped,
and the Green Man's said 'Hello', said
   'Hello'.
Look both ways, then walk across
while it is safe to go, safe to go.

*Suggest this song is used as a practical exercise in
road safety.*

PLAYGROUP VISITORS

A (police - man) came to play - group, he/sh came to say 'hel - lo'. He wished us all 'good morn - ing' and then he had to go. 'Good morn - ing, good morn - ing' and then he had to go.

A (policeman)* came to playgroup,
he/she came to say 'hello'.
He/she wished us all 'Good morning'
and then he/she had to go.

90

'Good morning, good morning'
and then he/she had to go.

*Nurse, postman, dentist, doctor,
milkman, fireman, etc.*

HOW TO PLAY

Choose a child to be the visitor, e.g.
policeman, nurse, postman, dentist,
doctor, milkman, fireman, dustman,
etc.

Lines 1–4:
Children dance round in a circle
holding hands, while 'policeman' walks
round the inside.

Line 5:
Children in circle stand still as
'policeman' shakes hands with one or
two of them.

Line 6:
'Policeman' leaves. Everybody waves.
New 'visitor' is chosen.

FIREMEN

(Tune: Skip to My Lou)

Verse 1

When the smoke be - gins to rise,

sparks and flames shoot through the skies.

Peo-ple di - al 9 9 9, then we have to go... So it is

Verses 2, 3, 4

One for the trou - sers, two for the coat,

three for the hel - met, strap near my throat.

Quick men, hur-ry af - ter me, down the pole so slip-pe-ry!

When the smoke begins to rise,
> *Adult and children crouch in open space.*

sparks and flames shoot through the skies.
> *Clap and quickly raise each arm in turn.*

People dial 999,
> *Pretend to use telephone.*

then we have to go . . . So it is
> *Stand up.*

One for the trousers, two for the coat,
three for the helmet, strap near my throat.
Quick men, hurry after me,
down the pole so slippery!

Rush to engine; jump inside.
Hold on tight, it's quite a ride!
When we get there day or night,
smoke and flames we have to fight.

We climb up ladders towering high
and then squirt water at house nearby.
Gradually the flames all die.
'Let's go home!' the firemen cry.

Mime the actions suggested by the words.

MONEY

First are the brown coins,
one p and the two.
Then next come the silver ones,
at least I think they do!
Five, ten, twenty and
funny fifty p,
followed by the golden pounds,
worth most to you and me!

Use coins to illustrate.

BESIDE
THE
SEASIDE

FISHING

Five — sil - ver fish-es — were swim-ming in the sea,

swim-ming in the sea, swim- ming in the sea.

Five — sil - ver fish-es — were swim-ming in the sea,

swim-ming in the wa - ter.

Chorus

A hun-gry fish-er-man came

sail - ing — a - long, sail - ing — a - long,

sail - ing — a - long. A hun-gry fish-er man came

sail - ing — a-long, and took one fish from the wa - ter.

Five silver fishes were swimming in the sea,
swimming in the sea, swimming in the sea.
Five silver fishes were swimming in the sea,
swimming in the water.

CHORUS
A hungry fisherman came sailing along,
sailing along, sailing along.
A hungry fisherman came sailing along,
and took one fish from the water.

4, 3, 2, 1.

No fishes left in that part of the sea,
part of the sea, part of the sea.
No fishes left in that part of the sea,
so the fisherman sailed back home.

[cont.]

HOW TO PLAY

Choose a child to be the fisherman, who waits to one side, i.e. the harbour, and five children to be fishes.

Verse 1:
Remaining children move slowly round in a circle with the fishes swimming in the centre.

Verse 2:
Stand still, face centre and clap, while fisherman sails round outside of circle before entering to 'catch' a fish and return with it to the harbour.

Last verse:
Fisherman 'sails' round the outside of moving circle.

Last line:
Stand still and wave as fisherman goes home.

LET'S STRETCH UP TALL

Let's stretch up tall like a lighthouse,
let's curl up small like a snail.
Let's spread our wings like a seagull,
and then be a boat with a sail.
Let's gallop along on a donkey,
let's go for a swim in the sea,
let's dry ourselves all over
and then have a picnic tea!

*Mime the actions suggested by the
words.*

PATTERNS ON THE BEACH

Look behind you!
Look behind you!
Patterns on the beach.
Running footsteps,
walking footsteps,
all within your reach.
Wiggles with your fingers,
squiggles with your toes –
as the tide comes in and out
all the pattern goes.

Look behind you!
Look behind you!
Patterns in the sand.
There are big marks
and little marks,
made by foot or hand.
Faces with your fingers,
letters with your toes –
as the tide comes in and out
all the pattern goes.

HOW TO PLAY

Adult leads children along
imaginary beach,
encouraging them to follow
the directions in the poem.

TEDDY AT THE SEASIDE

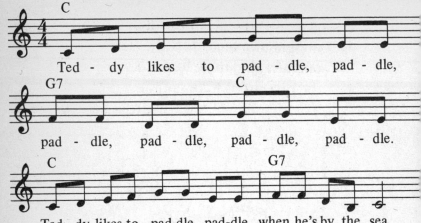

Teddy likes to paddle, paddle,
paddle, paddle, paddle, paddle.
Teddy likes to paddle, paddle,
when he's by the sea.

Teddy likes to jump the waves, etc.

Teddy likes to dig the sand, etc.

Teddy likes to look for crabs, etc.

Teddy likes a donkey ride, etc.

*Mime the actions suggested by the
words.*

TEN GREY DONKEYS

Ten grey donkeys standing in a line,
brushed, fed and watered,
and each one feeling fine.

Then (Emma) walked towards
them,
with money for a ride.
Oh no! thought Donkey Number
Ten,
and ran away to hide

9, 8, 7, 6, etc.

HOW TO PLAY

Children or fingers may be used to
represent the donkeys, with a
different child wishing to ride each
time.

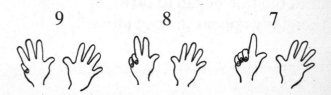

9   8   7

FIVE BLACK ROCKS

Five black rocks, sitting on the shore,
a wave came and covered one –
then there were four.

Four black rocks, sitting by the sea,
a wave came and covered one –
then there were three.

Three black rocks, nothing much to do,
a wave came and covered one –
then there were two.

Two black rocks, lying in the sun,
a wave came and covered one –
then there was one.

One black rock, alone – the rest had gone,
a wave came and covered it –
then there was none.

No black rocks, sitting on the shore,
until the tide began to turn –
then they appeared once more.

HOW TO PLAY

Choose five children to represent rocks. They
stand behind a curtain or similar (i.e. the sea)
held by adults and disappear in turn at the
appropriate time. Last verse all 'rocks'
reappear.

SANDCASTLE FUN

I'm going to build a castle
right here by the sea.
First of all it's very small,
and then it grows like me.

I'll add some towers and windows,
give a final pat.
Then run, jump and sit on it,
and knock my castle flat!

*Mime the actions suggested by the
words.*

BESIDE THE SEA

(Adapted from the song by J.H. Glover-Kind)

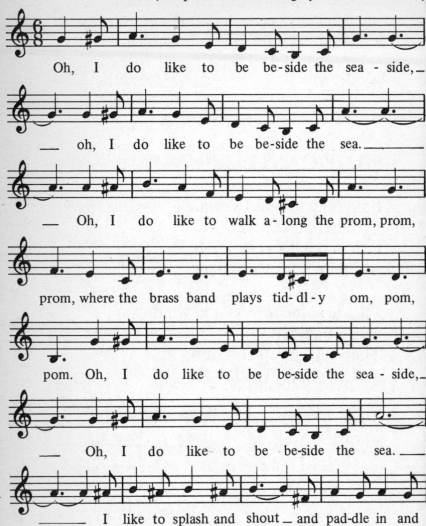

Oh, I do like to be be-side the sea - side,

 oh, I do like to be be-side the sea.

 Oh, I do like to walk a - long the prom, prom,

prom, where the brass band plays tid - dl - y om, pom,

pom. Oh, I do like to be be-side the sea - side,

 Oh, I do like to be be-side the sea.

 I like to splash and shout and pad-dle in and

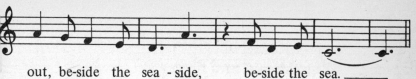

out, be-side   the   sea - side,   be-side the   sea. _____

Oh, I do like to be beside the seaside,
> *Walk round in a circle holding hands.*

oh, I do like to be beside the sea.
> *As line one.*

Oh, I do like to walk along the prom, prom, prom,
> *Release hands, but continue walking jauntily round in a circle.*

where the brass band plays tiddly-om, pom, pom.
> *Stand still, face centre, play imaginary instruments.*

Oh, I do like to be beside the seaside,
> *Walk round in a circle holding hands.*

oh, I do like to be beside the sea.
> *Continue as above.*

I like to splash and shout
> *Release hands, pretend to splash and shout.*

and paddle in and out,
> *Grip skirt/trousers and lift slightly as if paddling. Move towards circle centre and return.*

beside the seaside, beside the sea.
> *Continue paddling.*

IVOR THE DIVER

Ivor the diver
wears special clothes,
a wet suit and flippers
and mask for his nose.
A helmet and goggles,
then strapped to his back –
special breathing equipment,
an oxygen pack.

Ivor the diver
likes to explore,
under the waves
where he's not been before.
It's a strange, silent·world,
often hazy and dim –
a world full of fishes
and creatures that swim.

FAIRGROUND
FUN

TEN WOODEN HORSES

Ten wooden horses stand and wait
to hear the music play.
The roundabout begins to turn –
then one horse runs away!

9, 8, 7, 6, etc.

HOW TO PLAY

Use hands and fingers to represent
roundabout and horses.

CARNIVAL DAY

Hurray! Hurray! Carnival Day –
a big procession's on its way,
led by a band all dressed in red,
conducted by a man called Fred.
The majorettes are next in line;
they march along in perfect time.
Then come the floats, each with a theme,
all passing slowly like a dream.
Another band, a host of vans
and people with collecting cans.
Last of all the Carnival Queen –
what a splendid day it's been!

Mime the actions suggested by the words

THE BIG WHEEL

Um - pa - pa, um - pa - pa, let's pay our fare.

Um - pa - pa, um - pa - pa, strapped in our chair.

Rea - dy to fly like a bird through the air,

when we are at the fair.

Um-pa-pa, um-pa-pa,
Interlace fingers palms upward. Raise arms quickly in outward and upward motion.
Clap twice on pa-pa.
REPEAT.
let's pay our fare.
Hold out right, then left hand.
Um-pa-pa, um-pa-pa,
Repeat as line one.
strapped in our chair.
Mime action.

Ready to fly like a bird through the air,
Spread arms out to sides as wings.
when we are at the fair.
Clap.

Um-pa-pa, um-pa-pa,
Repeat as line one above.
feel the wheel go.
With hands linked, raise arms in outward and upward motion above head.
Um-pa-pa, um-pa-pa,
Repeat as line one.
look down below.
Mime action.
Let's give a wave to the people we know,
Wave.
when we are at the fair.
Clap.

DODGEMS

(Tune: John Brown's Body

Verse

Ov - er there's the dod - gems, let us

go and have a ride. In

eve - ry car there's room for two, when

sit - ting side by side.

Quick, the mu - sic's start - ing, they have

switched the pow - er on, so

dri - ver turn the wheel and let's be

Chorus

gone – let's be gone! Dod - ging, dod-ging, dod-ging,
dod - ging, dod - ging, dod - ging, dod - ging,
dod - ging, dod - ging, dod-ging, dod-ging, dod - ging, so
dri - ver turn the wheel and let's be gone.

Over there's the dodgems,
let us go and have a ride.
In every car there's room for two,
when sitting side by side.
Quick, the music's starting,
they have switched the power on,

[cont.]

so driver turn the wheel
and let's be gone – let's be gone!

CHORUS
Dodging, dodging, dodging, dodging,
dodging, dodging, dodging, dodging,
dodging, dodging, dodging, dodging,
so driver turn the wheel
and let's be gone.

Dodgem cars are dodging
round each other on the track.
Dodging cars to reach the side,
then dodging coming back.
Many times we bump a car,
smile, wave and make a friend.
This is fun, it's a shame
it has to end – has to end.

CHORUS
Dodging, dodging, dodging, dodging,
dodging, dodging, dodging, dodging,
dodging, dodging, dodging, dodging.
This is fun, it's a shame
it has to end!

*Mime the actions suggested by the words using
maximum space available.*

TOFFEE APPLES

Toffee apples, toffee apples,
Sticky round and sweet.
Toffee apples, toffee apples,
I've got five to eat.

4, 3, 2, 1.

HOW TO PLAY

Children or fingers may be
used to represent the toffee
apples.

HELTER SKELTER

One step, two steps, three steps, four,
five steps, six steps, seven steps more.
We must climb right to the top,
when we get there we must stop.

Put our mats down, take our place,
whizzing round and round we'll race.
Sitting straight, then lying low
to the bottom we will go.

Helter skelter – whizz, whizz, whizz,
what fantastic fun this is.
Helter skelter – whizz, whizz, whizz,
what fantastic fun this is!

*Mime the actions suggested by the words
using maximum space available.*

ROUNDABOUTS

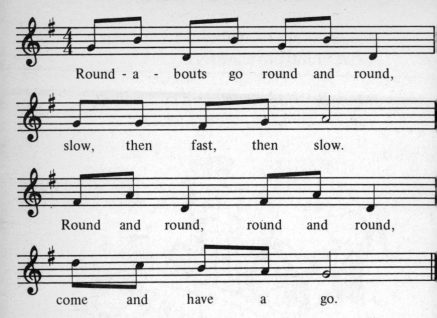

Round - a - bouts go round and round,

slow, then fast, then slow.

Round and round, round and round,

come and have a go.

Roundabouts go round and round,
slow, then fast, then slow.
Round and round, round and round,
come and have a go.

Roundabouts go up and down,
slow, then fast, then slow.
Up and down, up and down,
come and have a go.

Roundabouts go in and out,
slow, then fast, then slow.
In and out, in and out,
come and have a go.

Roundabouts go round and round,
slow, then fast, then slow.
Up and down and in and out,
come and have a go.

HOW TO PLAY

Form a circle, holding hands, and
respond to the instructions in the song.

Verse 1:   Change speed while walking
round.

Verse 2:   Go up and down on the
spot.

Verse 3:   Step towards centre of circle
and out again.

Verse 4:   Combine previous actions.

CANDY FLOSS

My mummy bought me candy floss
when I went to the fair.
I tried to eat it nicely,
but it got stuck to my hair!
It got stuck to my fingers
and it got stuck to my face –
the candyfloss was everywhere
except its proper place!

*Mime the actions suggested by the
words*

IN
THE
COUNTRY

HEDGEHOG LOG

Late at night
one hedgehog
walked along
a fallen log.
Lost his balance,
began to fall,
rolled himself
into a ball.

HOW TO PLAY

Pretend 'log'
drawn or placed
on floor. Children
are chosen one at
a time to be the
hedgehog.

FALLING FIR TREES

Five green fir trees all in a row.
Whoo–whoo–whoo
the wind does blow.
One tree begins to wobble
and then it starts to fall.
CRASH! (Clap)
So now there's only (four) trees standing tall!

4, 3, 2, 1.

Children or fingers may be used to represent the trees.

THE BEECH TREE

Chorus

In the mid - dle of a wood all a - lone a beech tree stood, do - ing what a beech tree should, blow - ing in the wind!

Verse

One lit - tle leaf came tumb - ling down, tumb-ling down, tumb-ling down. One lit - tle leaf came tumb-ling down and land - ed on the ground.

CHORUS

In the middle of a wood
all alone a beech tree stood,
doing what a beech tree should,
blowing in the wind!

One little leaf came tumbling down,
tumbling down, tumbling down.
One little leaf came tumbling down
and landed on the ground.

One little owl flew around, etc.

One little squirrel jumped around, etc.

One little mouse scampered round, etc.

One little rabbit hopped around, etc.

One little hedgehog shuffled round, etc.

and sat down on the ground.

[cont.]

HOW TO PLAY

Choose one child to represent the beech
tree, who stands with arms swaying in the
centre of a circle formed by the other
players holding hands.

CHORUS:
Lines 1–3:   Circle left.
Line 4:   Stand and sway imaginatively.
Animals, etc. gradually form inner circle.

VERSES:
A child/children are chosen to represent
the various animals, etc. They then make
the appropriate movements round the
beech tree. Other players watch and clap.
Repeat the chorus each time. The number
of leaves or animals can be increased
instead of changing the species, e.g. two
little leaves, three little mice, etc.

ANIMAL PLAYTIME

Five grey goats went out one day
in a farmer's field to play.
One ran too fast, slipped, banged his head,
then lay pretending he was dead.

4, 3, 2, 1.

No grey goats around to play,
till the farmer passed that way.
He gave each goat a little shake
and soon all five were wide awake.

Five pink pigs, etc.

Five brown cows, etc.

Five white sheep, etc.

*Children or fingers may be used to represent
the animals.*

FIVE SPECKLED FISH

Five speckled fish went out to play
in a silver stream one day.
One floated, dived and swam his best
and then lay down to have a rest.

4, 3, 2, 1.

*Children or fingers may be used to
represent the fish.*

THE FEATHER

Blow the feather gently,
> *Hold out one hand (palm upwards) with*
> *other hand, as feather, resting lightly upon it.*
> *Blow gently.*

hush, don't make a sound.
> *Raise index finger of 'feather hand' to lips*
> *and return.*

Watch it twirling, round and round,
> *Rotate 'feather hand' slowly downwards.*

softly to the ground.
> *'Feather hand' reaches floor.*

Suggest this rhyme is repeated after discussing
where feathers come from.

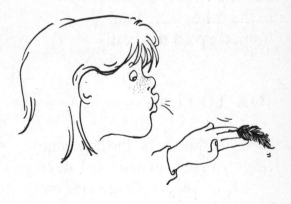

LAZY LAMBS

One day a lazy lamb was lying
on a bale of hay,
when another lamb skipped by
to see if she would play.
'No, thank you,' said the lazy lamb,
'but you could rest instead.'
So the other little lamb
jumped up on the bed!

One day (two) lazy lambs were lying
on a bale of hay,
when another lamb skipped by
to see if they would play.
'No, thank you,' said the lazy lambs,
'but you could rest instead.'
So the other little lamb
jumped up on the bed!

HOW TO PLAY

Choose a child to be the lazy lamb
lying on an improvised hay bale, e.g.
dust-sheet, rug, chalk drawing on
floor. Other children are chosen to be
lambs as required.

NIGHTLIFE

When children are asleep in bed
    Curl up on the floor.
and darkness fills the sky.
The creatures of the night wake up,
    Slowly uncurl, yawn and stretch.
as Mr Owl flies by.
    [Tu-whit, tu-whoo.]

They stop, they wait till he has gone,
then rabbits, mice and voles
    Sit up and point to each other.
creep out beneath the moon and stars
from burrows and from holes.
    On all fours proceed from holes with
    caution.

They rush around to find some food,
    Rush about.
then eat, then rest or play.
    Smile and dance.
But when they hear tu-whit, tu-whoo,
    Adult or child chosen to make owl sound.
they quickly run away!
    Children run to safety.

HOW MANY BIRDS?

Look at the birds up in the tree,
as high as high as they can be.
There's more than two.
There's more than three.
How many birds are up in the tree?

*Adult holds up fingers to represent
number of birds in the tree. At end of
rhyme, one child is chosen to count
them.*

CREEPY-
CRAWLIES

INSECT PARTY

We are going to have a par-ty, ____

we are going to have some fun, ____

(La-dy-bird, la-dy-bird, black and red ____

la-dy-bird) we do hope you can come. ____

____ Then we'll (walk) at the par-ty, ____ we'll

(walk) at the par-ty, ____ we'll (walk) at the

par-ty, ____ we'll (walk, walk, walk).

INVITATION
We are going to have a party,
we are going to have some fun,
> *(Ladybird, ladybird, black and red*
> *ladybird)**
we do hope you can come.

ACCEPTANCE
Then we'll (walk) at the party,
we'll (walk) at the party,
we'll (walk) at the party,
we'll (walk, walk, walk).

* Butterfly, orange/white, wave
  Grasshopper, greeny-brown, hop
  Bumble bee, yellow/black, buzz

HOW TO PLAY

Choose children to represent insects who wait to
one side.
INVITATION
Remaining players join hands and dance in a
circle. On hearing its name, the insect chosen
moves in its own particular way, round the
outside of the ring.
ACCEPTANCE
Insect joins circle, and all copy its movements.

BOATING BEETLES

One beetle in a boat,
one beetle in a boat.
If another went aboard,
would it sink or float?

Two beetles in a boat, etc.

*Children or fingers may be
used to represent the beetles.*

LET'S CRAWL

Let's crawl a - bout like a bee - tle. ____

Let's buzz a - bout like a bee. Let's fly a-bout like a

but - ter - fly, from tree to tree to tree.

Let's crawl about like a beetle.
Let's buzz about like a bee.
Let's fly about like a butterfly,
from tree to tree to tree.

Let's make a web like a spider.
Let's climb a wall like a fly.
Let's flit about like a wasp in and out
and zoom around the sky.

*Mime the actions suggested by the
words.*

SPIDER'S IN HIS WEB

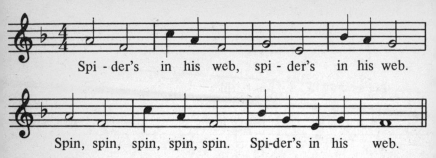

Spi - der's   in his   web,   spi - der's   in his   web.

Spin, spin,   spin,   spin, spin.   Spi-der's   in his   web.

Spider's in his web,
spider's in his web.
Spin, spin, spin, spin, spin.
Spider's in his web.

Spider wants a fly, etc.

Fly wants a friend, etc.

Beetle cuts him free, etc.

They both go home for tea, etc.

HOW TO PLAY

Choose children to represent a
beetle and a spider. Other players

hold hands in a ring with 'spider'
in the centre.

Verse 1:
Circle slowly left.

Verse 2:
Circle slowly right. At end of
verse, 'spider' chooses 'fly'.

Verse 3:
Circle slowly left while 'beetle'
scurries round the outside.

Verse 4:
Stand facing centre, making
scissor movements with arms as
'beetle' rescues fly.

Verse 5:
Children clap as the two friends
leave 'web' and skip hand in hand
round outside of circle.

LUCKY FLY

(Tune: She'll Be Coming Round the Mountain)

I'm a spider and I'm waiting for a fly.
If you come into my web you're going to die.
Do not struggle, do not shout,
I will never let you out!
I'm a spider and I'm waiting for a fly.

(Buzz, Buzz – got you!)

Fly was caught so first of all he gave a shout!
  (Help!)
Struggled hard and turned his body round
  about.
With his legs he gave a kick
where the web was not so thick.
Fly was lucky – he was soon seen flying out!

HOW TO PLAY

Choose children to represent:
'A spider' who sits in the centre of a circle
formed by the other players holding hands.
'A fly' who buzzes round the outside.

Verse 1:
Circle right. At the end of verse 'fly' enters
'web'.

Verse 2:
Stand facing inwards and mime actions of fly.
'Spider' pretends to lay table, etc.

POLLEN HUNT

(Traditional)

We must find some pol - len, ___ we must find some pol - len, ___ we must find some pol - len, ___ as we have done be - fore.

We must find some pollen,
we must find some pollen,
we must find some pollen,
as we have done before.

In and out the flowers,
in and out the flowers,
in and out the flowers,
as we have done before.

Choose a friend to help you,
choose a friend to help you,
choose a friend to help you,
as we have done before.

144

Fly back to the beehive,
fly back to the beehive,
fly back to the beehive,
as we have done before.

HOW TO PLAY

Verse 1:
Choose two children to be
'bees'. All other players hold
hands and circle left as 'bees'
fly round the outside.

Verse 2:
Stand still holding hands, and
raise arms to let the 'bees' fly
in and out.

Verse 3:
Clap while 'bees' each choose
a friend to help them collect
pollen.

Verse 4:
Circle right. 'Bees' fly round
the outside, entering the circle
at the end of verse.

WOODLICE WORLD

Guess what we saw in the woods today?
Five small woodlice out at play.
Susie, the first one, said, 'Let's run.'
Charlie, who chased her, found it fun!
Willie said he'd rather crawl,
while Jimmy rolled into a ball.
Then baby watched as he uncurled,
beneath the trees in Woodlice World.

*Children or fingers can be used to represent
the woodlice.*

ON THE MOVE

Along the path, a silver trail
left by Amadaeus Snail,
to help his friends all find their way
for he moves house three times each day!

*Children or fingers can be used to represent
the snail.*

A BIG BUSY BEE

My fingers are flowers full of pollen.
My thumb is a big busy bee.
It buzzes about, takes nectar out
and turns it to honey for tea.

Use both hands to interpret this rhyme.

ONE LITTLE CATERPILLAR

One little caterpillar said,
'I'm hungry, I must go and find some lunch.'
Crawled on to a tasty leaf,
munch–munch–munch–munch–munch!

HOW TO PLAY

One child acts the part of the caterpillar, or
alternatively a hand could represent the leaf for
one finger to 'crawl' along.

MONTY MOTH

Monty Moth was hungry,
so he found a woolly coat.
Gobble, gobble, gobble,
but a bit caught in his throat.
He coughed and coughed and spluttered,
wiped his mouth and flew away.
The coat had been delicious,
he'd be back another day!

Mime the actions suggested by the words

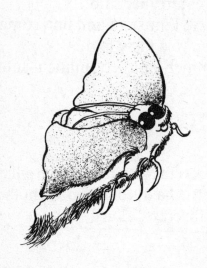

HELLO
ME

HELLO ME

Look in the mirror, and what do you see?
Adult holds mirror for a child to look in.
A girl/a boy
and I'm three/four
and that girl/boy is ME!
Child responds, with help if necessary.

OBSERVATION

Open your eyes and what do you see?
I see a (name of object) in front of me.

Is it square, or is it round?
Quiet, or does it make a sound?
Hard or soft, big or small?
Will it break if it should fall?

*A variety of objects may be used to
stimulate discussion.*

BIRTHDAYS

Birthdays! Birthdays! Oh, what fun!
A whole year passes, then you're one.

Birthdays! Birthdays! Cake for you!
A whole year passes, then you're two.

Birthdays! Birthdays! Presents, tea!
A whole year passes, then you're three.

Birthdays! Birthdays! Friends at door!
A whole year passes, then you're four.

Birthdays! Birthdays! Cards arrive!
A whole year passes, then you're five.

Birthdays! Birthdays! Oh, what fun!
There's one each year for everyone.

Use fingers to represent the passing years.

TRAINING

Whe-ther sun - ny or rain - ing we're
al - ways out train-ing, to keep our -selves health-y and
fit. _____ From the top of our heads to the
tips of our toes, we ex -er-cise each lit -tle bit! __
Bend and stretch one, two, three, bend and
stretch one, two, three, we ex-er-cise each lit-tle bit! ___

Whether sunny or raining
Stretch arms in an upward and outward movement to represent sun. Wiggle fingers to indicate rain.
we're always out training,
Jog on spot.
to keep ourselves healthy and fit.
Jog on spot.
From the top of our heads
Touch head with both hands.
to the tips of our toes,
Touch toes with both hands.
we exercise each little bit!
Twist body from left to right with arms outstretched.
Bend and stretch – one, two three,
Touch floor, stretch arms high above the head and clap one, two, three.
bend and stretch – one, two, three,
Touch floor, stretch arms high above the head and clap one, two, three.
we exercise each little bit!
Twist body from left to right with arms outstretched.

BOOTS AND SHOES

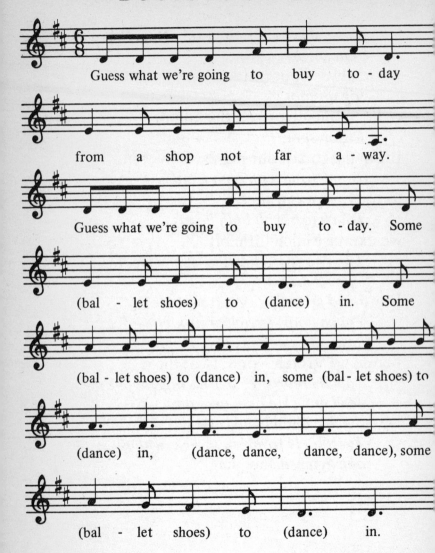

Guess what we're going to buy to-day

from a shop not far a-way.

Guess what we're going to buy to-day. Some

(bal - let shoes) to (dance) in. Some

(bal - let shoes) to (dance) in, some (bal - let shoes) to

(dance) in, (dance, dance, dance, dance), some

(bal - let shoes) to (dance) in.

Guess what we're going to buy today
from a shop not far away.
Guess what we're going to buy today.
Some (ballet shoes) to (dance) in.

Some (ballet shoes) to (dance) in,
some (ballet shoes) to (dance) in,
(dance, dance, dance, dance),
some (ballet shoes) to (dance) in.

Football boots to kick in.
Leather boots to walk in.
Big tough boots to climb in.
Trainer shoes to run in.
Army boots to march in.
Slippers soft to creep in.
Wellie boots to splash in.

HOW TO PLAY

Lines 1–4:
Children hold hands and form two lines,
which move towards each other and
back again as they sing.

Lines 5–6:
Stand still and clap.

Lines 7–8:
Mime the appropriate action.

DIRTY TEETH

(Tune: Frère Jacques

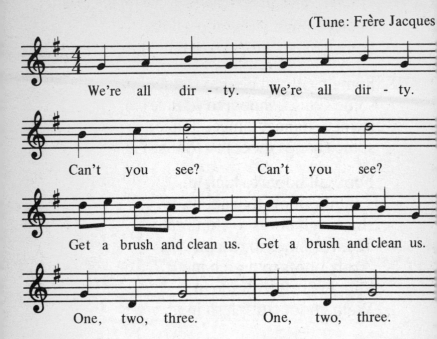

We're all dirty. We're all dirty.
Children kneel in circle (mouth) and bang on floor with hands.

Can't you see? Can't you see?
Point to each other.

Get a brush and clean us.
Pick up pretend toothbrush and use.

Get a brush and clean us.
Pick up pretend toothbrush and use.

One, two, three. One, two, three.
Brush one, two, three.

That feels better. That feels better.

Stand, then jump up and down on the spot.

Now we're fine. Now we're fine.

*Stand still. Touch shoulders and head with
both hands, then clap.*

Shining in the morning.

Hold hands and circle left.

Shining in the evening.

Hold hands and circle left.

All the time, all the time.

Hold hands and circle left.

POORLY FINGERS

This thumb was feeling poorly,
this finger was much worse,
so I took them to hospital
where they could see a nurse.
Nurse called for the doctor,
Doctor cured the pain,
so I telephoned to finger small
who took them home again!

*Point to the thumb and then each
finger in turn.*

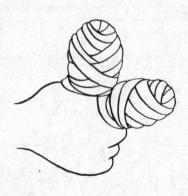

PLAYTIME

FOLLOW ME

Follow, follow, follow me.
Hop, hop, hop – one, two, three.
Bend your knees,
then stretch up high
and paint a rainbow in the sky.

Follow, follow, follow me.
Jump, jump, jump – one, two, three.
Fold your arms,
then shake your head
and now pretend that you're in bed.

Follow, follow, follow me.
Clap, clap, clap – one, two, three.
Move your legs,
then turn around
and sit down quickly on the ground.

*Children following an adult participate
as suggested.*

HATS

One hat on my head,
as you can plainly see.
If I put another on,
how many will there be?

2, 3, 4, 5, 6, 7, 8, 9.

Ten hats on my head,
as you can plainly see.
If I take (one) of them off,
how many will there be?

9, 8, 7, 6, etc.

*In order to help children
appreciate the mathematical
connotations of this rhyme,
suggest visual aids are used.*

TOYS NIGHT OUT

I've of - ten heard a ru - mour, I've

of - ten heard it said,— that

toys get up and move a - bout while

child - ren are in bed.— First of all they

nod their heads and then they stretch and

bend,— slow - ly straight - ening

up a - gain to shake hands with— a friend.—

I've often heard a rumour,
I've often heard it said,
that toys get up and move about
while children are in bed.
First of all they nod their heads
and then they stretch and bend,
slowly straightening up again
to shake hands with a friend.

The soldiers go out marching,
saluting one by one,
while monkey keeps them all in time
by banging on his drum.
The dolls go to the kitchen
to make a pot of tea.
Jumbo mixes up a cake
to share with you and me.

Teddy gets into a car
and drives fast out of sight,
while Disco Duck enjoys herself
by dancing through the night.
But all too soon it's over,
the last star fades away.
All the toys go back to sleep
as children wake to play.

*Suggest children may like to mime the
actions suggested by the words.*

BLOWING BUBBLES

I like blowing bubbles
which start off very small.
They quickly grow and grow – then POP!
There's nothing left at all!

Pretend to blow a bubble. Clap when it pops.

THE TRAIN

Let us make a diesel train
to go along the track.
An engine and ten carriages
to take us there and back.

One carriage first and then another,
three for my sister and four for my brother.
Five for me and six for you,
seven is red, and eight is blue.
Nine comes next and then it's ten.
Diddle-le-dum,
let's start again.

*Children or fingers may be used to play this
game.*

FIVE FURRY TEDDY BEARS

Five furry teddy bears
sitting on the floor.
One lay down, so that left four.

Four furry teddy bears
sitting on my knee.
One slipped off, so that left three.

Three furry teddy bears
sitting on my shoe.
One fell in, so that left two.

Two furry teddy bears
trying to catch my thumb.
One gave up, so that left one.

One furry teddy bear
crying all alone.
Dried his tears, then took him home!

*Use fingers or teddy bears to illustrate
this rhyme.*

FINGER SPORTS

Most thumbs like to go swimming,
while index fingers run.
Middle fingers kick at balls,
the next find tennis fun.
But the smallest of the fingers
are not keen on sport at all,
they would rather be like
Humpty,
just sitting on a wall!

Use hands to interpret this rhyme.

COUNTING BRICKS

One brick, two bricks,
three bricks, four.
Two and two
make four bricks
more.
Four and four
and two make ten.
Let us start
to count again.

[cont.]

*Use wooden
bricks/blocks to
demonstrate the
mathematical
connotations of this
rhyme.*

THE ROYAL FAMILY

Let your thumb be a king
wearing a crown,
your finger his queen
in fine jewels and long gown.

Then comes their son,
the young prince tall and fine,
then princess, then baby,
who's last in the line.

*Raise thumb and fingers of one
hand in turn to represent each
member of the family.*

THE
WORLD
OF
ADVENTURE

SKI-ING

(Tune: Three Blind Mice

Come ski with me, _____ come ski with

me, _____ o - ver the snow, _____

o - ver the snow. _____ You move your left ski and

then your right, you pick up your poles and hold

on to them tight. Fast - er and fast - er down

hills of great height, a - way we'll go. _____

Come ski with me,
come ski with me,
over the snow,
over the snow.
You move your left ski and then your right,
you pick up your poles and hold on to them
    tight.
Faster and faster down hills of great height,
away we'll go.

Come ski with me,
come ski with me,
water's so blue,
water's so blue.
Fasten skis to your feet, left then right,
just keep them together and hold the rope
    tight.
Towed by a boat leaving patterns of white,
away we'll go.

Mime the actions suggested by the words.

COOKING POT

Find a spark, light the fire. Watch the
flames get-ting higher. Brr, it's cold! Ouch, it's
hot! Let's put (car - rots) in the
pot. Put in one, put in two. Now what
else have we to do? Stir it fast! Stir it
slow! Who would like to have a go?

Find a spark, light the fire.
> *Stoop to light fire.*

Watch the flames getting higher.
> *Rise slowly, indicating height of flames with hands.*

Brr, it's cold!
> *Point to pot and shiver.*

Ouch, it's hot!
> *Point to pot – withdraw arm quickly.*

Let's put (carrots) in the pot.

Put in one, put in two.
> *Walk in towards centre and out again as the two 'carrots' are put into the pot.*

Now what else have we to do?
> *Continue going in and out.*

Stir it fast!
> *Turn inwards and pretend to stir as stated.*

Stir it slow!
> *Turn inwards and pretend to stir as stated.*

Who would like to have a go?
> *New ingredients are chosen from volunteers, e.g. apples, biscuits, raisins, chocolate, onions, etc.*

[cont.]

HOW TO PLAY

Players stand in a circle facing centre, where a hoop has been placed or a chalk circle drawn, i.e. cooking pot. Explain principle of game and ask for suggestions. Then choose two children to represent 'carrots', etc., who are removed from the circle at the end of verse one, to be 'cooked' at the beginning of verse two.

LITTLE ISLAND

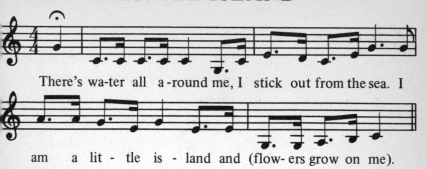

There's wa-ter all a-round me, I stick out from the sea. I am a lit - tle is - land and (flow- ers grow on me).

There's water all around me,
> *Find a space and turn round slowly with*
> *arms outstretched to sides.*

I stick out from the sea.
> *Stand still, move arms horizontally to front,*
> *fingers touching.*

I am a little island
> *Palms down, slowly lower arms.*

and (flowers grow on me).*

Mime actions of the verse chosen using all
the space available, e.g. fishes swimming.

* people build on me.
  fishes swim round me.
  birds fly over me.
  lions roar on me.
  children dance on me.

THE CROCODILE

I thought I saw a croc - o - dile a -
creep - ing up on me. I
did, I saw a croc - o - dile as
plain as he could be. His
eyes went flash, his jaws went crash, he
want - ed me for tea! That
mean old, green old croc - o - dile, a -

creep - ing up on me.

I thought I saw a crocodile a-creeping up on
   me.
I did, I saw a crocodile as plain as he could be.
His eyes went flash,
his jaws went crash,
he wanted me for tea!
That mean old, green old crocodile,
a-creeping up on me.

HOW TO PLAY

Choose someone to represent the crocodile.
Children stand with adult in a group a short
distance from the 'crocodile', who advances
slowly towards them. Group retreats at same
pace until the last line when everybody runs. All
players mime the actions.
Eyes flash – beak movements with hands near
eyes.
Jaws crash – clap hands together with arms
outstretched.
For tea – rub tummies.

ISLAND BOY

Boy is hungry –
he must eat,
pulls on hat,
jumps to feet.
Slings a basket
over arm,
runs towards
nearest palm.
Clings on tightly,
up he goes,
using both
his hands and toes.
Coconuts he picks
with care.
Slides down tree,
then eats his share!

Mime actions
suggested by words.

UP AND DOWN THE MOUNTAINS

Down the mountain – up the mountain,
down the mountain – up.
Down the mountain – up the mountain,
down the mountain – up.

REPEAT

Starting with thumb of left hand, go up and down in between the fingers with index finger of the other hand and return.

179

FIVE BANANAS

Five ba-na - nas on a ba-na - na tree,

three for you and two for me.

Let's go and eat them down by the sea.

Five ba-na-nas from the ba-na - na tree.

Chorus

Ripe ba-na-nas, ripe ba-na-nas, ripe ba-na-nas for

you and me. Ripe ba-na-nas, ripe ba-na-nas,

ripe ba-na-nas on a ba-na - na tree.

Five bananas on a banana tree,
three for you and two for me.
Let's go and eat them
down by the sea.
Five bananas from the banana tree.

CHORUS
Ripe bananas, ripe bananas,
Ripe bananas for you and me.
Ripe bananas, ripe bananas,
Ripe bananas on a banana tree.

Four bananas on a banana tree,
two for you and two for me.
Let's go and eat them
down by the sea.
Four bananas from the banana tree.

CHORUS

Three bananas on a banana tree,
two for you and one for me.
Let's go and eat them
down by the sea.
Three bananas from the banana tree.

CHORUS

[cont.]

Two bananas on a banana tree,
one for you and one for me.
Let's go and eat them
down by the sea.
Two bananas from the banana tree.

CHORUS

One banana on a banana tree,
half for you and half for me.
Let's go and eat them
down by the sea.
One banana from the banana tree.

CHORUS

No bananas on the banana tree,
none for you and none for me.
So we can't eat them
down by the sea.
No bananas on the banana tree.

*In order to help children appreciate the
mathematical connotations of this song,
suggest visual aids are used.*

PENGUINS

Five black and white penguins
were waiting for their tea.
One felt really hungry,
so he/she dived into the sea.

4, 3, 2, 1.

*Children or fingers may be used
to represent the penguins.*

PIRATES

There are no pi - rates a - ny- more, a -
part from just us few. So
if there is bad work to do, it's
up to me and you. So
grab a sword and jump a - board, it's
up to me and you.

There are no pirates any more,
apart from just us few.
So if there is bad work to do,
it's up to me and you.

So grab a sword
and jump aboard,
it's up to me and you.

We see a ship go sailing by.
It's full of jewels and gold.
We start to chase, we win the race,
then steal all we can hold.

So grab a sword
and jump aboard,
we'll steal all we can hold.

*Suggest adult assumes role of
pirate chief and carries out actions
of song with the children.*

TENT TROUBLE

(Tune: Grand Old Duke of York)

Each time we go to camp,____ we have to pitch a tent. ___ But it is not an ea-sy job, we won-der why we went!

Chorus

For when it's up it's up _____ and when it's down it's down __ and when it's on-ly half-way up, it's nei-ther up nor down!

Each time we go to camp,
we have to pitch a tent.
But it is not an easy job,
we wonder why we went!

CHORUS
For when it's up it's up
and when it's down it's down
and when it's only half-way up,
it's neither up nor down!

We take the tent from bag
and spread it on the ground,
but when we try to put it up
the tent pegs can't be found!

CHORUS

At last the job is done,
we smile instead of frown.
We have a rest, the wind gets up
and blows the whole tent down!

CHORUS

*Mime the actions suggested by the
words.*

INDEX OF FIRST LINES

ACKNOWLEDGEMENT

The author gratefully acknowledges the following for their help and support:

Christine Taylor, Theresa Gande, George Hammond, Maureen Stoneham and the children and staff of the Humpty Dumpty Playgroup.